The Holy Goat
of Gillespie County

by
Barbara Fay Brock

Illustrations by Daryl McDaniel

CORONA PUBLISHING COMPANY
San Antonio / 1989

Corona Publishing Company
   1037 South Alamo
      San Antonio, Texas 78210

Library of Congress Catalog No. 88-64097
ISBN 0-931722-73-X
Manufactured in the United States of America

CONTENTS

The Holy Goat
of Gillespie County

The Holy Goat
of Gillespie County

I HAD SOME COUSINS that grew up on a goat ranch up in the Hill Country. One cold spring they bottle-raised a baby goat in the kitchen after its momma died. Well, now, that goat never did get over living in the house. He sort of held it over the other goats and they were pretty much taken in by it. Kind of like he'd had a college education or something.

Now you may not believe this, but there are some parts of Texas that are worse about being Catholic than Baltimore and these cousins of mine were like that. So, naturally, their goats were too. When it came time for Saint Agatha's Feast Day, my cousins fixed up that hand-raised goat with wild flowers and ribbons made out of quilt scraps and took him to the church yard where the priest sprinkled holy water on him. When that goat got back to the ranch he told the other goats that he'd been ordained a priest. They were simple country goats so they were

1

pleased to have their own priest.

Of course, you can guess what happened next. He told them that they had to go to church ever Sunday. They were real good about doing that because they didn't have to go anywhere. They were already where they were. So he'd just start preaching at them. Of course, being goats they didn't know when it was Sunday so he just preached at them whenever he took a notion. Then he made it up that they couldn't eat prickly pear on Fridays. Them goats loved prickly pear and when they found out it was a sin to eat it on Fridays, they loved it all that much more. Since they didn't know when Fridays were either, sometimes they'd have Fridays two or three times a week. The main thing was that them goats knew he was looking out for their best interests.

Well, one day the yard gate got left open and that goat remembered the kitchen where he had been raised. He headed straight for it like a shot. The little children had left the screen door off the latch so all he had to do was give it a little butt and walk in. Once inside, he did some reminiscing about his early days. He recollected how fine and warm and loving that kitchen was and how my cousin Verna May had taken such gentle care of him till he was big enough to go out and be with the herd. He recognized the place under the tall stove where his box had been and he sighed when he recalled the way my cousin used to

2

give him all the warm milk he could hold from a big old rubber teat.

He mouthed and chewed everything that he was curious about, and he was thinking about heading on back out to his congregation. He was going to tell them about his visit to the house where he'd been raised—just so as they wouldn't have occasion to forget his special background. Well, being a goat he picked the wrong door. Next thing he knew he was in an entirely different place, with lots of people eating and drinking and smoking and talking and laughing and decorating up a cedar tree.

The people started yelling and swearing and making ugly gestures at the goat. Everbody was chasing him in different directions as fast as they could go. That goat got pretty confused. There was even a fire in that room and it smelled awful to him. Well, that goat lost his dignity and began to run like crazy up and over the furniture, anywhere to get away. Now, my aunt was a great one to crochet. She had crocheted doilies and antimacassars and table cloths and sideboard cloths all over the place. When that fool goat tried to butt his way through a divan he got one of those antimacassars hung up on his horns. The thing had tassels that hung down in his eyes and drove him into a conniption fit. My cousin Verna May threw the front gallery door open and when that goat smelled fresh air everbody had to get

out of the way. Antimacassar and all, he was out the door.

When that dern goat got back to his flock with that crocheted antimacassar hanging from his horns, they all of them wanted to know what had happened to him. That goat had the presence of mind to tell them other goats that he'd been made up from a plain priest to be a bishop.

Well, now, that's a true story or if it isn't it ought to be.

The Devil Machine

MY OLDEST COUSIN (we called him Little Orville because he was named after his daddy) he got hisself a scholarship to go down to The University and play football. One of the alumni of The University gave him a brand new pick-up painted red and it was so shiny you could see yourself in it as good as a mirror. Little Orville kept polishing that pick-up all the time he wasn't practising football or studying to sign his name on the papers his tutors fixed up for him. When ever he'd come up home he'd park near the windmill and just as soon as he'd had a bowlful of his momma's peach cobbler and clabber and a cup of coffee with his daddy he'd go out and warsh and polish up that pick-up 'til dinner time.

Sometimes after supper he'd let my younger cousins and the mojados, who never got to go nowhere, get in the back of the pick-up and ride around on the ranch. After dark they could spotlight jack rabbits with the headlights. Once in a great

6

while the goats would get in the headlights and just freeze there staring at the lights like they'd never heard of barbecued goat.

Now this all gave occasion to that hand-raised goat to do a lot of preaching. He had started in calling his preaching a sermon but that didn't change things, it was still just preaching. One of the things that he preached against was that pick-up. He told them simple country goats that it was a machine of the devil and it had come after them because of their sinful ways. He told them how he knew some of them were getting after the prickly pears on Fridays and worse yet that they were squeezing under the orchard fence and chewing the bark off the young peach trees. Even thinking about that was a venial sin. He preached at them about this sin and that sin ever Sunday and at all the prayer meetings 'til he got them to feeling real guilty.

It was the Saturday a week after Hallowe'en when Little Orville came up late after he'd played a football game where he'd been a star. He'd broke one boy's leg and gave another one a concussion and he was feeling very good. When he came up the lane from the road and parked his pick-up by the windmill he accidently ran over the water trough and it split open and the water spilt and ran all over the place. It had been a pretty good sized water trough. When Little Orville tried to get down from his pick-up he must of

7

slipped, I guess, because he fell flat on his back. We all laughed fit to kill because it took everbody even the mojados to get him up and onto the porch where he decided to sleep. Little Orville was sort of like a two-ton bull; when he decided to sleep somewhere we didn't argue with him. His momma brought him some feather pillows and some old quilts and covered him up because the nights were starting to get cold before daylight.

Now the next morning, just when the sun was coming up over the rocky hill, that hand-raised goat led his flock down to the water trough like he did ever other morning. You can just imagine when they saw that devil machine with the first sunlight bouncing off its side door and the water trough all split and spilt and they smelled the gasoline fumes and the water all churned up with the caliche where Little Orville had slipped down, they just liked to of died of fear. And the more they looked the worse it got. There wasn't just one devil in that machine, there was a whole flock of devil goats looking back at them right out of the side of that pick-up. And at the head of that flock was a devil goat with his beard and horns and long ears flapping back and forth like a windmill with a broken chain. Naturally they were seeing their own reflections but they were just goats and they couldn't of known that.

The more they looked the more skittery they got.

8

That bishop goat couldn't stand the insolent way that devil goat looked at him. So, blowing his lips till they turned wrong side out and showed off his yellow teeth, he cocked his head down and took off straight at that pick-up. He raised up on his hind feet and launched hisself right straight at that devil goat and butted him horns on. There was an awful crash just like somebody had hit the side of Little Orville's pick-up with an eight-pound sledge. That goat bounced off the side of the door like a football throwed against the side of a barn. He hit that wet slippery caliche and each of his legs went off in a different direction. His nose went down in the mud and dug a furrow nearly a foot long before he stopped skidding. His eyelids just fell down over his eyes and his long curley eyelashes lay real still on his boney cheeks like as if he was dead. All them other goats just looked and looked at him and got even more nervous because, I guess, they must of thought the devil had won that one.

Little Orville had been sleeping there on the porch, you remember, and when he heard somebody bashing his pick-up, well, he came up off that pallet and ran out of the yard towards his truck like he'd run the day before down the football field. When he saw that fool goat and the dent in his pick-up door he was plumb astounded. First he cussed that goat and then he started in to laugh till he was so weak he had

to lean up against his truck. For years, ever time he'd tell about it he'd start in to laugh again. He'd say that when that goat opened his eyes they were looking right crossed and he figured the goat had a worse headache than he did.

Little Orville tied that goat up to the yard fence with a little bitty rope that any little kid could of chewed through in five minutes but that goat just stood there all that morning my aunt said, like some kind of Christian martyr. Finally, she untied him and shooed him back to the other goats that had all gone off down to the gravelly creek, which was running again.

Well, you may not believe this, but when that goat got down there he climbed up in that big old bent-over oak tree that he had taken to using for a pulpit, and he told those simple country goats that he'd wrestled with and slain the devil in that pick-up. And then they had a big prayer meeting and it was while they were singing hymns that he first noticed what a pretty clear voice one of the sopranos had. But that's another and awfully embarrassing story.

Romance on the Rocky Hill

I BET YOU THINK a goat can't fall in love. Well, you're wrong, because I saw that hand-raised goat knocked hind end over tea-kettle in love with a little Spanish milk goat.

Ever time he'd climb up in that old bent-over oak tree down by the gravelly creek, and go to preaching about how he had wrestled the devils in Little Orville's pick-up, why, she'd look up at him and her eyes would get so bright that sometimes he'd lose his place in his preaching and have to start all over again. And when she'd bleat out hymns in that lovely lilting soprano voice, he'd practically get the blind staggers and fall out of his pulpit. He seemed to think her very presence perfumed the air and he'd breathe deep and sort of sigh through his front teeth. He prayed for her to go forth and be bountiful and multiply—a lot more than he did for any of the other does. I don't mean so as they noticed; they just stood there and chewed and scratched and flapped their ears. Goats are real tolerant about things like that.

Well, my cousin Verna May, got invited to the semi-formal dance given by the students of Our Lady of Poverty High School. I offered to loan her one of my dresses but my Aunt said she didn't think that the Sisters of Divine Inspiration that ran the school would care for any of my dresses. So, Verna May borrowed a real pretty green dimity dress from one of my other cousins down in Dripping Springs. Since she had to sew it up a little everwhere so as it would fit her, it looked practically like new. The only thing wrong with the dress was that it smelled real strong of cedar chest. So Verna May hung it out in the yard on the clothesline to let it air out in the sunshine.

Goats don't like to eat off the ground. They much prefer to bite the leaves off of the bushes. Anything fluttering overhead looks very inviting to them because it could be some new kind of bush that they haven't tasted before. It was a good thing that the yard had a stout fence around it or the goats would of chewed all the clothes off of the line ever Monday. As it was they'd stand outside the fence and look at them clothes all Monday afternoons with first one eye and then the other, just like chickens looking at sow bugs. And that's just the way they stood and looked at Verna May's borrowed green dimity semi-formal dress.

Now, there was a culvert in back of the house

and it made a gap under the fence that wasn't big enough for the goats to get through but they knew it was there. That little Spanish goat, that the hand-raised buck was so in love with, was littler than the other goats and maybe smarter too. She just squeezed her way under there, I guess, just for the fun of it. All the goats watched her chew the whole ruffle off the bottom of that green dimity semi-formal dress. I don't think they figured she'd get in any kind of trouble either. That hand-raised goat hadn't ever preached a word to them about not chewing the semi-formal dresses on the clothesline. I guess he'd just never thought of it or he didn't reckon it could be done.

Well, after that little Spanish goat had chewed, pulled, ripped and torn the ruffle entirely off that dress she came on back out through the culvert and she had a swag of that ruffle with her. That bishop goat must of preached a good bit about tithing, because she brought that swatch right to him and he mouthed it over pretty good.

Of course, circumstantial evidence has convicted more than one innocent party and a goat in Texas is guilty until proven innocent. Verna May came along just about then and she saw her dress all torn up and that billy goat with a piece of it hanging out of his mouth and she was fit to be tied.

You see, she was the very one that had hand-raised that little buck goat in the kitchen and fixed

14

his bottles in the middle of the night and doctored him when nobody else thought he was going to pull through. She'd made him up a mustard plaster and sewed it into an old sock and seen to it that he kept it on his little chest when he was a helpless little baby. She'd lost a lot of sleep over him. So when she commenced to yell at him and she told him she was going to sell him for enough money to buy herself a dress at the store, he knew she meant ever word of it.

It got real quiet. All the goats knew what selling meant. They'd seen a plenty of goats sold. It meant that that goat that got sold got tied up in the back of a pick-up and went for a ride and didn't ever come back home. You can just feature how upset they were to think their priest and bishop would be gone for good. But more than anything, that hand-raised goat was upset because it was him that Verna May was going to take for a ride, and just when that little Spanish goat was about to come into season.

He did what any right-thinking goat would of done. He took off like a streak of greased lightening and Verna was right behind him all the way. He dodged behind the windmill and circled the water trough twice and then he took off up the rocky hill with his ears, beard and tail sailing on the wind. Verna May was getting red in the face but that was just because she was mad. She wasn't winded a bit, she was a country girl and plenty smart at catching goats. When that goat took the right hand side of a big limestone outcrop, Verna went for the left and was going to head him off at the other side.

Just about then she heard the sound of a rattler shaking about ten big buttons on his tail. Well, you can believe she came to a dead stop. There isn't anything that can bring you to a dead stop quite the same as a really big rattlesnake, especially one that's all coiled up with his tail in the air and rattling them buttons. Verna May told us that she knew she was done for and that that semi-formal dress didn't seem near as important as the prospect of getting snake-bit.

Now, I don't know if you understand how bad goats hate rattlers. And maybe that hand-raised goat saw a chance to get back on Verna's good side. Anyhow he came around that limestone outcrop in one beautiful leap. A couple of feints and he had that snake so mixed up it like to of broke its fangs off striking at the rocks where the goat had just been. The next thing that snake knew, the goat was all over him with four hard sharp hooves.

They had to put that rattler back together to measure him. Three and a half feet long with ten rattles—although the last time I heard Verna May tell about it it had grown some. My cousin, Little Orville skinned it out and made hisself a real nice hat band.

Of course, Verna May gave the rest of the dress to the goats. She hung it on a spiney bush up by the limestone outcrop so as they could chew on it whenever they wanted to.

Verna May wore one of my dresses to the semiformal dance and it was O.K. because my aunt crocheted her a fascinator to cover up her bosoms when the nuns were looking. And that was the night she first went out with Lloyd Untermeyer who she is married to now.

The little Spanish goat was so impressed with what that buck goat had done that she came into season early. That goat walked around on his toes with his legs all stiff and dancy, and kept blowing kisses at the little Spanish doe. She seemed to think he was very romantic. She had a kid out of that season and it was a beautiful thing to see how she raised it to be a Catholic.

How The Holy Goat
Got His Name

I KNOW YOU'RE WONDERING how come that hand-raised goat don't have a name. Well, it's because my uncle was a goat rancher. To him them goats weren't pets, they was livestock. Whatever livestock think and do on their own time don't matter as long as it don't interfere with getting the job done. So if this goat seemed important to hisself and the other goats and to us, that don't mean he was anything special to my uncle except to tell stories on.

But he did finally get a name. School had started and Verna May and Carley John and Verleen and Little Albert were going into town to Our Lady of Poverty High School. But the little children were going to the public school that was just down the road a piece, because money was a little scarce that year. The quickest way for them to go was to cross the pasture and go over the fence and cut across to the road, so the mojados built them a ladder kind of a

19

thing to go over the fence and they were supposed to remember to pull it over after theirselves so as they could get back over in the afternoons. But of course you can guess what happened. When they left the ladder up one day, that hand-raised goat went right over it like it was nothing and all them other goats followed like he was leading them to the Promised Land. Maybe the little children knew about it and maybe they didn't. Anyways the goats all got to the school house and went right in. Somehow the door had got left open.

The sad thing about all this was that the class had a new teacher from San Antonio and she got alarmed by a herd of goats in the school house. Them goats had such an appetite for knowledge! They sure did cost the State of Texas a whole new set of readers, and another new teacher.

That winter it came on real cold. The almanac had said it was probably going to be the coldest winter in a long time and although goats are a lot smarter at taking care of theirselves than people, when it keeps on being cold and maybe wet they can get sick and you can lose some of them. So my uncle had the mojados build what he called the winter quarters; a real stout shed with good sound walls and a clean dirt floor and mangers for feed and a pretty good amount of space for the goats. But someway they just didn't fancy the idea of going in there. Some of the goats had gotten the idea that they were going to have to stay there all winter and they were willing to fight for their freedom.

It was of an evening and a blue norther was coming down and everbody wanted to get them goats under cover. My uncle and the mojados and all of us did the best we could. We pushed and pulled and hollered and begged and whupped up on them goats, but they wouldn't see reason. I'd show them feed in my hand and they'd just grab it and whuffel it onto the ground and run around like they was being stabbed with knives. We tried to explain that they were only going in for over the night but they'd got so worked up that they couldn't hear thunder. You would of thought that hand-raised goat would of been the best of all to go inside since he'd been raised in the kitchen, but he was the sorriest of the lot.

Our heads were aching and our hands were sore and we'd been kicked and butted in so many places we were sick and tired of goats in general, but it was clear something had to be done. The mojados kept telling my uncle to make the Judas do it. But my uncle and all of us just thought they was cussing out that hand-raised goat. Finally Big Tony took ahold of my uncle's jacket, pointed at his eye, pointed at my uncle's eye, pointed at his own chest, pointed at that hand-raised goat, and then he pointed at hisself again. Then he started to imitate that goat. He did such a good imitation of that goat that we all took our hands out of our pockets to clap and laugh and holler. Then Big Tony started for the winter quarters and he motioned to everbody to follow. The rest of the mojados fell right in line and went in and me and Verna May and Carley John and Little Albert and Verleen and the rest of the little children all went in just like the Rodeo Grand Parade.

Little Orville said to my uncle that he thought they meant that that hand-raised goat could lead them other goats into the winter quarter. My uncle said, "Fine, how'r we going to convince that goat he wants to do that?"

Big Tony came back out of the winter quarter and he went up to my uncle and put his thumb to his mouth and closed his fist and raised it up in the universal sign. He said, "Tequila?" My uncle said, "Schnapps," then he went in and brought out a bottle about half full.

Big Tony picked that hand-raised buck goat up under his arm and with that schnapps bottle in his other hand he bent over and went into the winter quarter and closed the door.

It seemed like we waited a long time and occasionally we would hear Big Tony singing ranchero songs and we were pretty sure that hand-raised goat was singing along. It was almost suppertime before Big Tony and the goat had come to some kind of an agreement.

Ever after that if a blue norther was blowing in, Big Tony would holler, "Vente aca, Judas," and then he'd clank that old schnapps bottle and that Judas goat would bring his congregation into the shelter from the storm. Then that hand-raised goat would preach and preach on moderation, temperance, and abstemiousness.

The Least of These

EVERY RANCH HAS its barn cats. Some of them are pretty rough customers, being just the next best thing to wild. There was one old yellow tom everbody called Old Fighter. He'd whupped up on so many raccoons, possums and dogs, not to speak of cats, that both his ears had got chewed clean off. His tail had a sharp right turn in it and he was missing whole patches of fur. He was ugly as unrepentant sin but he was smart.

Children, this cat was a mouser. When my uncle would move the hay bales in the hay shed, Old Fighter could catch mice five at a time, one with each paw and a spare in his mouth. He wasn't cruel, they never knew a thing. He was so quick they didn't suffer a bit. Nor would he eat hardly a one of them. It was like a sport to him. He just did it for the joy of it, sort of like Teddy Roosevelt.

The one animal Old Fighter didn't mess with was that hand-raised goat we called Judas. The feeling was one of mutual disregard. It was like they were

25

both too uppity for the other one to tolerate.

Well, what happened was there was a family of mice that had moved out of the field into the winter quarter and had lived there for a season. They had taken to listening to Judas preach and they dearly loved the sermon on doing to the least of these. They'd nibble away on the goats' feed and, talking with their mouths full, they'd chirrup on about how they was the least of these and because of this it was owing to them. They were entitled to it. They were cute and little and sort of pink in their ears and tails and they were so poor.

Judas preached about how the poor will be around even unto the end of the world and he told his goats that they were laying up treasure in heaven for sheltering these smallest and poorest of the barn creatures. His voice soared militant in his sermons on beating off the Godless cats with their deadly claws and bloody jaws. He instructed his congregation to be careful with their hooves and not to trounce the baby mice that were beginning to hatch out in pecks and bushels.

When it got to where they were squeaking and skittering so as to become a nuisance, then Judas began to suggest to them that they return to the fields where there was more room and they could visit with their cousins, where they could gather bits of nuts and berries and natural organic foods just like they

had done before they came to live in the winter quarter. But they said they were best off right there by Judas' warm side and they didn't want to go out in a cold dusty field because they never liked their kin folks half as good as they loved the goats and the winter quarter and listening to Judas preach about giving all his worldly goods to the least of these.

When he saw that wasn't going to work, Judas began to preach at them mice about going out into the world to seek their mission and fulfill their vocations and carry the good news. The mice would only answer in the cheerfullest way that they was the least of these and it was owing to them, just like Judas had preached. And they were going to be around even unto the end of the world. Them mice didn't seem capable of theological discussions and Judas began to wonder if they had rational minds and immortal souls. The other goats had been real tolerant of the mice chewing on their hair and getting under their feet and into their feed, but they were beginning to get awful tired of it. Trouble was brewing sure as varmints is varmints. Judas wondered if there had been some kind of misunderstanding. It sure was a puzzle.

It was of a Sunday and he was leaning on the water trough, sipping a little and watching the perch that the little children had put in there to catch the mosquitoes, and he was thinking. While he was thinking, a voice came down to him from above. "You dern fool goat, you ain't got the sense God gave them Pedernales perch." Old Fighter was lounging on the water tank and looking down at Judas with something more than contempt. Well, now, that cat started in quoting chapter and verse, Old Testament gospel at Judas till he went weak in the knees with envy.

"Tolerate not those that defile wherein you dwell. Smite the ungodly. They neither chew the cud nor are their hooves cloven. They are vermin and are not of your tribe. They are a pestilence and they are sown to be reaped."

"I hadn't never thought of it just that way," Judas allowed.

So that evening while Judas carried on a vigorous prayer meeting down by the gravelly creek, which was running again, the commotion that went on in the winter quarter made the ruckus at San Jacinto look like a ladies' pink tea party.

My uncle used to laugh till the house shook when he'd tell about it. He'd say those were the most surprised mice in Gillespie County when Old Fighter and his troops descended onto the walls of Jericho.

How Judas Went Out
To Save the Heatherns

AFTER THEIR TRIP to the school it wasn't so easy for the goats to go visiting. My uncle had told the mojados to make sure all the fences were stout and solid. Going off the ranch was not something that the goats were encouraged to do.

But one day when all the goats were bunched together near the road fence Judas saw his opportunity and he took it. "Up jumped the Devil." He jumped onto the backs of the other goats and right on into thin air. Like a champion pole vaulter he flew through the air in a beautiful arc. He cleared the top bob-wire with all but one little tip of one hind hoof. That was enough to upset the parabola of his flight and he landed like a sack of meal. His parishioners heard an awful thump and a great whoosh of air and when they looked through the road fence they saw their fallen priest who neither spoke nor cried aloud. He lay there and after awhile they heard one little squeaky hiccup. They were worried and puzzled so they just chewed their cuds and flapped their ears and waggled their tails in an encouraging way. One of the wise old nannies quoted, "And don't pride just always go before a fall."

When Judas come to good and got his voice fairly back to normal he commenced his farewell sermon. He explained to them how they was saved and salvation was theirs and they knew all he could teach them about sin and guilt and what not to do and when not to eat prickly pear and when Sundays was and how to do novenas and all. And he told them that he had heard the call to go out into the wilderness and preach to the other heatherns and carry the good news to the poor pagan babies and all them that in darkness dwell. He preached at them about their responsibility to be concerned about the spiritual welfare of goats all over the county that might be without the blessing of having their own bishop to tell them what to do. There were tears in his voice as he bid them a last farewell, but by then he'd gone on so long that most of them goats had got more interested in topping off the huisache buds.

Now, I know you're worried about him getting road-killed but you'll remember he had had experience with Little Orville's truck and he feared with a healthy fear all the machines of the Devil. So don't worry about that, there was plenty of other trouble for him to get into.

He walked a good ways down the side of the road before he came on two cows and a good-sized calf and he announced to them how he was a renowned preacher and how it was that he was going to save them. And he started in to preach. They listened a while and said amen at the proper places but after a while they sighed with regret and said they thought he was sure a fine spit-fire preacher but that they were already saved and pretty soon they had to get on in to get milked. Judas said that it was morning yet and cows didn't get milked till evening, but they said that they liked to get an early start. So Judas went on his way.

A mile or so down the road he saw the sorriest, roughest looking bunch of rag tag goats you'd ever want to know about. Those goats was penned up in a corner of a pasture by the road fence and there was an old black and white dog that had them completely buffaloed. Ever time one of them goats would so much as shuffle a hoof that old dog would growl and they'd step right back in line. It was a sad sight to see their rights to life, liberty and happiness being abused like that and Judas knew he was where he'd been sent to. If they wasn't heatherns in bondage he didn't know what was.

He studied on the situation for a long spell and then he went over to the fence and he started in.

Goats, he told that dog, were noble animals of intellect and breeding. They were the chosen breed and were meant to govern and not to be governed. He went on till that dog's ears and tail were completely beat down and that poor repentant animal slunk over to the fence with the humblest of hang-dog looks. You'd of cried to see it.

Old Judas rejoiced to see that sinful dog coming to be saved. That dog's elbows was clear up over his back bones when he eased under the fence. "Come on, heathern, and be saved!" That bishop goat turned a positively benign countenance to that old dog as he came near enough to get blessed.

It was just about then that them sorry-looking goats cried out, "Arriba! Baah-ya con Dios." In one flash, like a revelation, he knew that them sorry-looking goats was sheep and obviously Christians and also he noted that that old dog had launched hisself off the ground and was flying through the air right at his head like a cannon ball with fangs. That old near-sighted dog must of thought Judas was a trickster wolf and he was going to take him in for the last roundup.

Well, no tired old dog with a herd of sheep to tend can out-run a goat that has a clear understanding of the lay of the land. Pretty soon the old dog left off and headed back to his sheep. It was a good while though before Judas slowed down enough to look backwards.

HOW JUDAS WENT OUT AND SAVED THE HEATHERNS

Old Judas was winded and tired but he kept on searching for deserving heathern sinners, but mile after weary mile there wasn't nothing but orchards of peach trees in bloom and acres of wild flowers. Evening came on and he hadn't seen hide nor hair of any genuine heatherns and he was thirsty. He came up on to the strangest gravel pasture he'd ever seen. Machines of the Devil were lined up in a row. If he could of read the sign he'd of known he was at the County Line Tavern and Cafe honky-tonk. There was plenty of good-old-boys hurrahing around in the parking lot and he went right up to them figuring they'd get him a drink. Them boys thought it was pretty hilarious to see a goat guzzling down beers from old Lone Star long necks so they accommodated him. After just a few beers he got so silly that they went in and telephoned my uncle to come get his fool goat.

Well, now, there are those who will tell you that you can learn a lot by traveling around but sometimes what you'll learn don't always hold water. When that goat got back home he told them other goats, between giggles and hiccups, that it wasn't no use being a missionary because there ain't any heatherns in Texas.

The Judas Goat
and the Radio Preachers

THE WINTER THAT the mohair futures hit an all-time low was the same one that was always remembered as the coldest winter for one hundred years. It got so cold that winter that Dr. Pepper would freeze when you'd pour it into the cup so you'd have to use an ice pick on it before you could drink it. The water trough froze so the goats would get up on it and stomp it through to get a drink. And all the mojados went back to Mexico till Spring.

When my aunt heard there wasn't going to be much use trying to sell the mohair that year she got some extra biddies on account of she knew that they might need her egg money before the year was out. Everbody said that having a radio in the chicken shed helped to get the hens to lay more. So she got her a battery radio and put it out there by the nests.

Now you know my aunt was real religious and

she wanted her hens to be uplifted. She put the radio on the radio preacher station from Clute, Texas. Any time you were anywheres near the hen house you could hear them radio preachers carrying on like their livelihood depended on it.

"Keep them love gifts coming."

"Sinner, sinner, sinner let us hear from you. Keep them cards and letters coming—no matter how small or how large your donations, they will buy you a ticket to the river Jordan and the Promised Land."

"Come be warshed in the blood of the Lamb."

"Bringing in the Sheep,"

"Little Brown Church in the Wildwood,"

"Throw Out the Life Line,"

"Sinner, Come Home."

There was lots of hymn singing and it was all in whole notes and very close harmony—just beautiful. Judas and his lead soprano, the little Spanish goat, sang along and all the goats learned all four verses to nearly all their favorites.

There were lots of offers to sell exciting things like genuine simulated diamond rings and statues of your favorite saint that could glow in the dark or sit on your dashboard but bad as them goats wanted them things they couldn't figure how to send off for them.

Judas was more than a little concerned about the number of his own congregation that was attending to his Sunday sermons with their ears turned toward the chicken coop. And that's how the problem arose. Judas and the rest of them goats listened to the radio from the chicken shed but what do goats know about radios? So they came to the conclusion that it was one of the chickens doing the preaching and singing and from their experience with chickens they considered it to be a sure enough miracle. Judas would go to the hen house and look in through the chicken wire. He'd turn his head sideways and study on first one of them chickens and then another. He figured it must be some mighty powerful chicken, but he sure didn't see a likely one. Ever day he'd watch them chickens

scratching around in the yard squawking and clucking and he'd study on it and figure but it just didn't seem likely to him. There wasn't a chicken there that had enough sense not to look up during a rain storm. What Judas came to want more than anything else was to see one of them chickens really preaching or singing hymns or at least speaking in tongues.

Now my uncle wasn't too keen on radio preachers and one day he changed to the news and weather station. Ever after that, what with the news and the weather, Judas had his hands full just keeping up prayer meetings to take care of one calamity or another that the chicken house announced until finally the batteries wore out.

It was always a mystery to them goats what had happened to the voice from the chicken house. But Old Judas never could be friends with a chicken after that.

Lenten Devotions

CATHOLICS START WORRYING about Easter a
long time before it gets there, on account of they have
Lent. Some years they seem to have more Lent than
others and that hard year that was the coldest winter
in one hundred years they sure had a lot of Lent.

Judas had his work cut out for him. He preached
about how, for their sins, they weren't supposed to eat any
prickly pear or peach tree leaves and them goats just got
all dreamy eyed remembering when there was leaves on
the peach trees and the prickly pears wasn't all frozen and
long gone. He told them how, for penance, they wouldn't
have any molasses in their feed and they coughed up their
little meager cuds and tried to remember when was the
last time they'd had molasses in their feed.

There wasn't hardly anything left on the ranch for
anybody to eat, much less the goats. Ever time we went
up to see my cousins we carried food enough for an army
and my mama always said she sure was glad Little Orville
was getting fed by The University or we'd of had to of

pulled a trailer. But my daddy'd say we owed it to them because they was family.

The goats was sick and tired of staying in the winter quarter, and even with the extra heavy coats they'd grown they had got so poor and skinny they shivered like they was doing the shimmy when ever the wind was out of the north and my uncle would call Old Judas to bring them in. Days they would paw around and chew the twigs off of what ever was left standing that they hadn't already chewed down to the ground. They were even climbing up in the cedar trees to strip off the sour tasting evergreens and eating the seeds off of the ground.

The comeuppance of all this was that my uncle realized he was going to have to sell the goats before they starved. It hurt all our hearts to think about selling the goats on such a sorry market. We sure hated to think about them going for sausage. But the worst of it was that that hand-raised Judas priest goat got wind of it someway.

Now he worried about it a lot. He was most worried about losing his congregation, which he had taken to calling his parish, and of maybe not being a priest-bishop anymore and maybe never getting to be an archbishop at all. Well, you can believe that that goat decided to do something about it.

He preached them goats a sermon about the deliverance of the Israelites in the wilderness, and the manna from heaven, and the parting of the Red River, and the manna from heaven, and the burning bushes, and the pillar of fire, and the manna from heaven and the pillar of clouds by day and the manna from heaven, and for once them goats really paid him a lot of attention; and they prayed to be delivered from Lent like the Israelites.

They prayed like all get-out and the little Spanish goat led the hymns and them goats sang fervently:

> "In the day of the Lord, we will put our
>   hooves together.
> We believe Spring will come if we put our
>   hooves together.
> We'll stand at the manger and pray with
>   each other.
> And the manna will fall if we pray with
>   each other.
> And a nice burning bush for to warm our
>   flanks and withers.
> And a pillar of fire for to warm our
>   ears and whiskers."

That night it rained like a fish and it was warm rain from the Gulf of Mexico. The next day the sun was so hot that the brush started swelling up knobs that turned green before the end of the day.

That Easter Day the goats nibbled and sighed and made eyes at each other and sang, "Na-a-a-a-men, Na-a-a-a-a-men, Na-a-men, Na-a-a-men, Na-a-a-men all the day long."

So that coldest winter in one hundred years finally got over. The goats had all grown shaggy, dirty,

lumpy, tangled coats that looked awful and smelled worse. That Judas goat looked just like a prophet from the Old Testament with his beard blowing in the wind. He could of been painted on the ceiling of a Italian church and he'd of looked fine. He'd stand up on a rocky outcrop and preach about dwelling in the desert on honey and locusts. Which was almost as pleasing to the goats as his manna from heaven sermon. Along about then a tad of honey would have been mighty comforting but my aunt was keeping back what was left for medicine in case some of the little children got sick.

Things were still pretty tough for my aunt and uncle and my cousins. The goats could get by pretty good eating off the land but prickly pear and chaparral won't do so good for people. If it hadn't of been for Little Orville's sending home money from his allowance at The University where he was spring training (they were going to let him start over again at The University so as he could play football some more) well, if it hadn't of been for his allowance things would of been mighty slim.

The weather had steadied down to mostly warm days with only once in a while a freeze at night, so the mojados came back. One morning there they were. They said things were pretty hungry in Mexico. My uncle told them times were hard on the ranch too and maybe they'd better keep going but they didn't. I think they was tired out and glad of a safe bed and my aunt's cornmeal and they liked goat meat pretty good.

Well next morning, since they hadn't never heard of mohair futures being low they commenced as usual, to shear. They started with the strongest and toughest of the goats and the does that weren't about to kid. And I bet you have already figured what majestic Old Testament prophet got clipped first crack out of the chute. He fought and kicked and snorted and peed, and in general made a fool of hisself. Afterwards he looked about like a new inductee at Fort Sam Houston who'd just got his first Army haircut. He was a lot littler than he'd seemed like and the scissors had snipped his skin in a few places and me and Verna May had doctored him with gentian violet and volcanic oil so he had purple polka dots to add to his other indignities. The other goats took to laughing at him behind his back. But he knew it. You could of seen right off that he was embarrassed. If there'd of been a fig tree anywheres around he'd of got ahold of a leaf or two and covered hisself up.

Now, in Texas you never know what the weather's going to do. It can be warm as anything and suddenly out of the north can come a cold front that'll drop the thermometer right straight off the side of the barn. Of course, that's exactly what it did.

That evening that poor shivering shorn prophet

45

called a special prayer meeting in the winter quarter, but him and his parishioners that had been clipped were shivering so and their teeth were chattering so and they were feeling so down and sorry for theirselves that old Judas just couldn't get that service off the ground. The best they could do was to get into the winter quarter and bunch up together to keep warm.

The little Spanish goat was a nanny now and on cold nights my aunt took her into the kitchen to milk her. What she heard that night in the kitchen about how my uncle hoped maybe he'd get a little better price on their coats if he could sell them early. Maybe he wouldn't have to sell the herd. Everbody hoped he wouldn't have to sell the herd.

When she got back to the winter quarter she got that Judas goat up against her warm side and told him what it was she'd understood. He studied on it a while and then he got up on the manger and he preached at them goats a mighty sermon. It was all about offering up their shivering and their suffering for the sins of the world, and how that their sacrifice would not be for nought nor in vain. That they should go quiet and gentle to be shorn, he urged them to follow the example that he had set and be meek and mild to the mojados and that their coats would be coats of redemption and surely bring more manna from heaven, and maybe molasses in their feed again.

They sang a beautiful hymn. The little Spanish

goat sang the descant fine while the preacher goat sang a passable bass:

> "Be not afraid,
>> afraid, afraid,
>
> Your coats will bring a fat time,
>> fat time, fat time,
>
> Come follow me,
>> follow me, follow me,
>
> And we will feast the best,
>> feast the best, fe-east th-e b-est."

They sang a long time and they were pleased with themselves. My uncle went out to see if there was something wrong but he said he guessed they was just restless. But they slept good.

The next morning Little Orville was up home to help and they finished them off in a warm afternoon that brought out all the fragrance of those sacrificed coats.

Somewhere in Paris, France, that spring there was a lad with a delicate air who had decided that mohair was going to be the very thing for ladies' Fall wardrobes. Long sweeping skirts and coats and jackets and sweaters were going to make society girls happy for a season.

My uncle was nearly knocked flat on his back by the price he got for them coats. There's no way you've ever seen a happier man. He brought home things all of us had forgotten about. And he brought feed: oats and barley and soybean oil and meal and minerals to lick and best of all cane sorghum black strap molasses.

The Knights of Columbus Haul

MY UNCLE WAS a Knights of Columbus. That's sort of like a Mason or a Rotary Club, only Catholic. It seemed like their mainliest business was raising money. The money all went for good works and there was so much good works to do they were always raising money.

Well, what happened was they got up a church festival and my uncle got the mojados to fix up a goat cart for my little cousins to ride in the parade.

I bet you know who got to pull it. At first old Judas was not too pleased with the privilege. I think he understood what was wanted, but he acted like a fool and would go the wrong way or not at all. But after my aunt got through with his Knights of Columbus blanket and hat and he had a look at hisself he got real good. The chicken feathers on the hat bothered him some. I think they reminded him of the radio preacher. The

49

little Spanish goat told him he was the handsomest goat on the place and everbody said so.

My uncle painted the cart with the Knights of Columbus colors and posted a handsome seal on the side and it looked very fine. My little cousins took turns riding that cart around the ranch roads for practice 'til they like to of wore old Judas out, and my uncle had to pull the damper on it some.

When the festival day came, my uncle got on his tuxedo and his shiny shoes and his Napoleon hat with the feathers and his special sash that showed he had a degree and his sword and he marched with the other men right behind the goat cart. There wasn't hardly any breeze but the flags they carried looked beautiful like they were made out of silk. The high school of Our Lady of Poverty had a boy's drum and bugle corps and they had some of the boys carrying banners too. And, oh, it was a sight.

They marched right down the middle of Main Street and Judas did hisself proud. Ever time they came to a cross-street they'd stop and the drum and bugle corps would do some about faces, and the Knights of Columbus would do some little bitty steps, and the little child that had been riding would have to get down and another little child would get to get in and ride for the next block. My cousin Carley John would pull on Judas' rope and hold the feed in front of his nose. But I bet old Judas could of marched the whole way by hisself.

Judas was the hit of the day and by the time they got back around to the church yard, everbody at the festival wanted their children's pictures taken in that goat cart with that fancy goat in his Knights of Columbus regalia. Judas was bringing in money for good works faster than you could say skat. The only event that was even half holding a candle to the goat cart was the 4-H showing of prize-winning sheep and goats and that's what started the trouble, you see.

Just about when all the bar-b-que and tamales and sausage-on-a-stick and beer and snow-cones was sold, and there was just a few pecan pies and jars of pickled peaches left, that buck goat Judas took to raising his upper lip and blowing out his breath real strong and kind of stretching out his neck and snuffing the air. Well, just about then the Mayor's daughter, Trudy, who nobody liked much anyway because she was sort of prissy, was having her picture took. That hand-raised Judas priest goat started off across the church yard, pulling the cart with Trudy in it. He headed right to the 4-H show.

Sure enough, before you could get out of the way, he'd found romance again with the prettiest of all the blue-ribbon nannies. Them two goats commenced courting right in the shadow of the church and before little Trudy and everbody. The Mayor's wife was hollering fit to die for little

51

Trudy to get down out of that cart and my aunt was hollering at my uncle to make Judas quit. But little Trudy was hanging on to that cart and watching the whole affair with more interest than I could account for, and my uncle was leaning up against the beer booth, limp from laughing so as he couldn't hardly stand up.

When the dust had settled some, Father Hubert, who had raised goats hisself before he went to the seminary, said he guessed it was alright because that nanny belonged to the Grossmachers, who were Lutherns, and he could see that Judas sure had made

a convert.

Little Trudy got an awful lot of teasing about her goat cart ride at school the next week, but she took it real good. She quit being so prissy and in fact when she was a southmore at Our Lady of Poverty High School she got picked to be a cheer-leader for the football team that won district.

Oh, yes, and that nanny goat she dropped twins and the Grossmachers gave one of them to Verna May who hand-raised it in the kitchen.

Old Fencebuster

IT WAS OF a morning right after the 4th of July and there hadn't been a drop of rain for a month. Just like any other morning, Judas was leading his congregation over to the water trough when all them was galvanized by the sight of an outlaw goat coming up the lane from the road. They looked at him through the lane gate and some of the young goats asked Judas how come a goat could be on the wrong side of the lane gate. That priest goat started in about how many are called but few are chosen and he preached on a while about minding his sermons and not committing any sins so as the gates of heavenly pearl would not be shut against them. He sure hated to admit he didn't know something.

That stranger sauntered along the fence line and cast a practiced eye on each fence post and picked one that was to his liking. It was an old post oak and termites had eaten away most of it underground. The stranger goat leaned against that rotten fence post and pushed it right over on to the ground. He came right on through that fence like you'd step through a prickly pear patch. Just like an oldtimey outlaw coming into a saloon.

Judas flapped his ears and sniffed and told that stranger goat he couldn't do that to their fence. That fence protected them from the road and the devil machines. It had always been there and they had a right to that fence because it was on their place. "You can't come in here and walk through our fence just like it wasn't there!"

The stranger goat just chuckled, sort of, and allowed as how he'd already done it and what was for breakfast.

One of the old does said that she thought they should take the young goats and head for the back end of the rocky hill to remove the occasions of sin, but Judas was as mad as a wet hen and he challenged that outlaw goat to a showdown.

Now that old stranger goat was a sorry-looking type. His hooves hadn't been trimmed in a good while and his coat was greasy and knotty and full of cockle burrs and it smelled bad. All the same he was big and under all that dirty hair he had tough stringy muscles. He was a regular outlaw. If Judas hadn't of been so mad he'd of thought twice.

The wise old nannies and the little Spanish goat started on up the rocky hill. They told each

55

other it was better not to encourage them. Judas continued snorting and pawing the ground and in general planning his strategy. All of a sudden he realized there wasn't anybody there. That outlaw goat was forty yards away leaning on my aunt's garden fence and it was starting to give. Judas snorted a couple of more snorts and pawed up a couple of more rocks and gave it up. He looked around, sort of shamefaced, to be sure nobody had seen him make a fool of hisself. Mercy! The garden fence was down and the old fencebuster was getting after the collard greens. Poor old Judas was as distraught as a chicken in a hail storm.

It was just lucky for that old outlaw goat that my uncle came out of the house about then. Uncle Orville picked hisself out a chunk of stove wood and went after that goat like Saint George went after them scaly dragons. He caught that old fencebuster and tied him up in a harness to where he sure couldn't get loose. Judas was real pleased.

My uncle called old Groosmacher and told him to come get his goat fast because the sorriest thing any rancher could do to another was to bust down fences and let his goats into another man's place. Even though he had a good water well Uncle Orville couldn't supply water to all the livestock in Gillespie County, much less prime collard greens. My uncle gave old man Groosmacher such a big piece of his mind that it was a good while before old Groosmacher could get it across that he didn't have any goat missing.

So my aunt called the sheriff and it was hardly any time 'til he came down the lane in his police car, sixty miles an hour with the lights flashing and the siren going and a dust cloud that reached almost all the way back to town.

Well, when my uncle explained to the sheriff how Judas had cornered that old fence-busting goat in the garden and alerted him to come on out, the sheriff made Judas a temporary county deputy. Well, you can believe that hand-raised goat felt fine. His only regret was that the other goats wasn't there to see the sheriff arrest that outlaw and put him in the police car.

You can bet on it, Judas told his congregation that evening at prayer service all about how he had been made a County Deputy—only leaving out the temporary part.

There's sort of a sad ending to this story. It seems like on the way back to town that outlaw jumped the sheriff who totally wrecked his police car and had to walk the rest of the way to town. That old fence-buster goat got clean away.

How Judas Made
Another Convert

EVER SUMMER MY UNCLE and his family used to
come on down to San Antonio and stay at the Menger
Hotel. They'd stand out on Alamo Plaza and watch
that neon cowboy up on top of Joske's department
store throw that lasso. My uncle always said it was
sure a wonder how he never missed. They'd do their
shopping and go to the movies and ride the street car
out to Brackenridge Park and see the Monkey Island.
They always had a big time. They didn't have to worry
about the ranch because the mojados were there and
they mostly did everthing anyway, and they didn't
ever go nowhere.

Except Sundays. Sundays they'd walk across
the fields to Martinez to go to Mass. And that's when
it all happened.

The goats and the chickens had the place all to
theirselves when this big old truck came up the lane
from the road. A cowboy got down from the truck and

unlocked the gate with a great big pair of pliers.

They drove up by the water trough and the cowboy got down and opened up the back end of the trailer and let down a ramp. There coming down the ramp was one of the slickest-looking goats them ranch goats had ever seen. I mean his hair was brushed. His hooves was shiny. His horns was polished. And he smelled of Bay Rum.

He started in to talk real smooth. What it all was was he was there for their benefits. He was a representative for The Apostolic Insurance Benefits and Trust Brotherhood Company, Inc. He explained how he was like a religious brother of an order that specialized in providing this insurance, benefits and trust and it was his mission to help all the livestock all over the county to get insurance benefits and he could sure be trusted as he was even the carrier for all the goats of the whole Archdiocese of Central Texas.

Insurance was a new idea for them goats and they couldn't think what they needed it for. Well, that slick-looking goat told them. He told them his company could insure against sickness of all kinds, accidents, dislocations, dismemberments, sprains, wrenches, broken hooves, the bloat and scours, indigestion, sterility, sore teats and mange. All they had to do was sign up and they were protected against these things right away as soon as they signed up and

if they couldn't write their names a hoof print would do fine.

That old hand-raised goat studied on this idea for a while and as he had gained some in wisdom, he figured there might be a catch somewheres so he asked what all that was going to come to.

The salesman was busy slipping around amongst the nannies, kissing the little baby goats and telling their mommas how pretty they were. He turned toward Judas and looked real respectful and honest as a seminarian and in a real educated voice he addressed Judas as Monsignor and he allowed as how the cost would be deferred. So Judas was satisfied on that count and asked just where they could put their hoof prints.

That city goat told them he had all the forms and the lists of limitations right up in the trailer and for them to just step right this way. Some of the old does thought maybe they'd just as soon do without the privilege but the salesman told them it was a group policy and if they didn't come on and sign up then everbody would be the loser. Judas tuned up and did a little sermon about not paying any attention to false profits and how females ought not to speak out of turn anyways. He led them goats right up into that trailer and was going to be the first one to do his hoof prints.

That smooth-talking goat kept calling them

sister and brother, just like they was kin, and when he had got all of them up into the trailer he asked the Monsignor to return thanks for their all being protected from all that sickness and injury. They hadn't no more than bowed their heads when the trailer doors closed up. The engine started up and the floor fell right out from under their hooves, and they all started in to holler. "Law Mercy! we're getting rustled."

Judas knew right then he'd been hornswaggled.

There was a lot of crying and criticism and hullabaloo but when that old Judas priest goat turned his eyes on to that insurance salesman everything got real quiet because they all knew old Judas might be a priest but he wasn't a conscientious objector. He was just boiling mad and his voice bounced off the sides of that trailer like a ricochet. He asked that smooth-talking goat how come he'd done such of a thing. Well, that city goat just looked him right back in the eye and told him it wasn't his fault, he was only doing what he was told to.

Judas was so plain disgusted that he looked around to his congregation so as they could see how disgusted he was. But when he looked at them he saw they were so afraid. He heard the old does telling their little goats to be brave and say their prayers because they was all together and safe. They told them it was just a big adventure to get rustled and to

get to ride in a real big trailer truck. Just think how
much fun it was going to be to tell them chickens
about it when they got back home. Why what a laugh
it was going to be to see them chickens drop their
beaks when they heard their story.

So Judas made up a litany and sang:

Priest: For being all together and safe
Response: Let us be truly grateful.
       P.:   For getting to ride in a big
              trailer truck
       R.:   Let us be truly grateful.
       P.:   For having a real big adventure
       R.:   Let us be truly grateful.
       P.:   For how the chickens are going to
              drop their beaks when they hear us
              tell about it
       R.:   Let us be truly grateful.
       P.:   For our brother goat who was only
              doing what he was told to,
              Let Us Pray:

And he started in praying out loud for that
swindler goat to see the light and come to the fold and
mend his wicked, two-bit, thieving, rustling ways 'til
that slick-looking goat was down on his knees and
crying like a baby.

Well, when they got to where they was going
them rustlers had an old holding pen that was just
about worn out. There was only one goat in that pen

63

and when them goats saw who it was, right then they all started in to sing Glory Halleluyah and Amen. And Judas started in on a fine sermon on the mysterious ways things happen. He quoted scripture, "Like the ways of a rock upon a serpent." On account of it was Old Fencebuster, that outlaw goat. Well, the rustlers drove on off to get their buyer and they weren't no more than out of sight good when that fence was down and the goats were on their way back home.

My uncle was sure surprised when he saw that herd of goats coming down the lane from the road. There was Judas and Old Fencebuster and a slick-looking show-quality goat leading the way and visiting with each other like old friends.

When Old Fencebuster saw the sheriff's new car parked there by the water trough, he allowed as how he had business some place else and he took off. But Old Slick stayed with us. My uncle called all over the county trying to find the owner of that show goat but nobody ever owned up. He used to chuckle and grin and tell us that old Slick was the most devoutly religious goat on the place.

Uncle Demi John

EVERBODY IN TEXAS has a drinking uncle to tell stories on. Mine was uncle Demi John.

It was a while after Easter, my uncle Demi John carried his wife, my aunt Rosie, up to the ranch on account of she was expecting their first child and she wanted to be with my aunt (who was her sister) when it came time. Everbody was walking on eggs for fear he'd fall off the wagon and shame hisself in front of the whole family.

Uncle Demi John never meant anybody any harm and he worked hard, right alongside the mojados, at anything my uncle set for them to do. But ever day it was getting closer to the blessed event and he was feeling very dry.

The little Spanish goat was getting heavy, too, and Judas could sympathize with uncle Demi John because he loved that little Spanish goat and he knew it was his fault that she was in trouble.

That day it happened, my aunt and her sister

went into town to light a few candles and start a flying novena for my uncle Demi John's sobriety and her safe confinement. They hadn't any more than gotten their head scarves tied on good than Father Hubert came over from the rectory to tell them they'd better get on back. My cousin Verna May had called and uncle Demi John was missing and everbody had looked for him and they couldn't find him. And, well, my aunt's bottle of medicinal whiskey was missing and they were sure worried about it.

They looked everwhere they could think of for poor uncle Demi John but he wasn't there. By now, though, you've surely guessed where he was at. Yes sir, there he was sleeping like a child, right in the middle of the goats' winter quarter all surrounded by the goats, warm as a skunk in the kitchen and lots more welcome. He'd shared his plug of Red Man Chewing Tobacco all around and they'd enjoyed it pretty much. The goats were pleased to have a guest and they gave him as good hospitality as they had and since he didn't require much everbody was pleased.

Come early morning the little Spanish goat told Judas that she thought it was time. Well, that hand-raised goat just fell all to pieces. He started to shake and got real pale around his eyes and his ears wobbled all around. As things progressed he almost fainted and he was, in general, more trouble than he was worth. Finally one of the old does got kind of short

with him and told him to go somewheres and pray and not to come back until they called him.

The poor little Spanish goat had counted on Judas to be strong and comfort her when it came time. She was pretty disappointed and looked real down at the mouth. What with all the commotion, uncle Demi John had waked up and he saw the shape the little Spanish goat was in on account of how old Judas had let her down and he petted her and talked gentle and calm and loving to her and rubbed her back and sang soft to her and he explained to her how come he knew old Judas was just scared and weak and worried and useless and guilty feeling and that that goat would be proud and brave again once it was over.

My uncle Demi John called Judas in hisself to see the little newborn baby goat. Old Judas lit up like a neon sign. That little Spanish goat was licking at that little buck goat's face and fluffing up his coat. Judas sighed real deep and commenced in to say that that heavenly washing would be that baby goat's baptism. He told the little Spanish goat that strength and honor were hers, that she could rejoice because ever time she opened her mouth wisdom and kindness came out. He told her someday her little Billy would rise up and call her blessed and Judas did too and he praised her till she had to put her head down to smile.

Now, you understand that uncle Demi John

hadn't ever heard Judas preach before and he was real amazed. But when all them goats started in hymn singing in four part harmony, he knew right then that he was going to go on the wagon for good. He took the temperance pledge and swore off for good and everbody in the family knew that he meant ever word he said.

I'd like to tell you he never touched a drop again but I can't. Just the same, he was the one man for my aunt Rosie and there wasn't anybody could help but like him when they saw how gentle and sweet he was with aunt Rosie and all that batch of children they had. Of which the first was born that spring, my little cousin Heidi Rose—you remember her. She was the one that put the Chinese-lady-finger firecrackers in the garland of flowers the fifth graders were holding the year the mayor's little daughter Trudy got to act out the part of the Queen of Heaven for the May Crowning.

Loco Weed

THE MOJADOS WERE WONDERFUL about growing things. As soon as they got to the ranch ever Spring they'd fix up my aunt's garden. They seemed to know how to do it just right and my aunt never had to tell them a thing. Ever year she won blue ribbons for her vegetables and she was very proud of them and always took the ribbons out and showed them to the mojados before she hung them up on the wall under Grandma's Certificate of Award from Governor Hogg for having seven sons for the Southland.

Right in the middle of the corn, where you wouldn't hardly notice it, they always grew a nice patch of marijuana, just for medicine. It was very good for belly aches and melancholy. Ever month when my aunt would go to the post office to mail a money order of their wages to their priest in their home town in Mexico, they'd play sad songs on their guitars and smoke a little, just to ease their miseries.

When the boys were little they used to smoke with the mojados some but as soon as they were big enough they preferred liquor or beer. Little Orville said it was sissy to suck on a little home-made cigarette when a real man would lift some old long neck Lone Stars. He allowed that some of the boys at The University smoked a little bit but that was just because they were in the Fine Arts Department.

Our mommas told us all to look out for real dope fiends whenever we were in town. Everbody knew the signs to look for: crazy eyes with pin-point eye-balls and real jerky motions and asking little children if they wanted candy. We all knew they'd commit any kind of crime, especially kidnapping little children to sell to the white slavers, because they were so crazed from dope, but we never did see any. I figured it was because they were all in New Orleans playing for jazz bands in houses of bad repute. But we stayed on the lookout for them. We used to scare ourselves to death talking about what would happen if we were ever to meet up with a real dope fiend.

That hand-raised goat never did get over want-ing to hang around people and he must of overheard us and maybe that's what caused all the trouble. Maybe he didn't understand the difference, after all, you have to remember, he was only a goat.

71

That summer when the marijuana was just going to seed and the corn was all played out and the rest of the garden was pretty well burned up, a bunch of the spring born kids who were pretty much adolescent goats by then, they got into the garden and ate up a pretty good amount of that marijuana. Well, their mommas caught them at it and they got so upset with them that they took them kids right straight to their priest, old Judas, for confession.

That hand-raised goat pulled hisself up on his holy orders and told them little silly kids that was the worst thing he'd ever heard about. He made them promise their mommas and him that they'd never be wayward dope fiends again. He preached at them and told them how it was that they were sure going to be gangsters and outlaws and even worse. He ranted at them 'til they'd of had belly aches for sure if they hadn't of eaten all that marijuana.

The way Judas kept on about it you'd of thought that they'd stole the flag of Texas down off the capitol dome in Austin or said a cuss word in the Alamo. Them poor guilty little goats were the sorriest little old goats you ever saw. Their little heads hung down by their knees and their eyes were half-shut and kind of brimmed with tears all the time. They didn't cavort and their tails hung down between their hind legs and they sighed a lot and said they sure were so sorry.

At first the mojados were mad at the little goats too because they'd eaten up nearly all the seeds and they were going to be hard put to plant another crop. But they knew what Judas didn't know and couldn't realize, that they were just little goats and so they forgave them and helped them all they could. Big Tony told them they ought to learn to try new things out a little bit at the time.

Their mommas were getting kind of tired of hearing about it. The other nannies whose kids hadn't been in the garden were acting prideful and making comments like, "acorns don't fall far from the tree," 'til there was hard feelings all around.

I don't really know whether the mojados talked to Judas or if it was the little Spanish goat that reminded him of his own visit to the County Line Cafe and Honky Tonk or if the mommas of the guilty little kids had a word to say or maybe that hand-raised goat just got some sense hisself, but, anyhow, he preached a sermon about forgiving for the 77th time, about the periodical son and how his daddy forgave him, about doing unto others and rejoicing in the warm bosoms of the family 'til even the guilty little kids who was being forgiven began to get restless and the little Spanish goat started in the hymn singing when Judas stopped a minute to draw breath:

> "Amazing Grace, how sweet the sound
> That saved a goat like meeeee . . ."

The goats went on back up to the feed yard to see what was for supper and it sure was a pure pleasure to see them little adolescent kids gamboling and cavorting and wagging their tails again.

Visiting Nobility

WEATHER IS ONE THING you can depend on in Texas. It's always a comfort to know that whatever weather you're having, pretty soon it'll be worse. Summer had come on pretty hot and dry. The gravelly creek was stone dry and the tank cock kept the windmill pumping just about constant so as to have enough water just to drink and wash once in a while. It was so dry the mesquite beans weren't fermenting and that was a disappointment to Judas and his congregation.

But like everbody says, just wait. That Sunday it all happened started out so dry that when my aunt and uncle and all the children drove off the lane to go to Mass it took an hour and a half for the dust to lay and there wasn't a cloud in the sky. Just after the mojados left off across the fields to Martinez where they would have Mass too, the wise old nanny with the broken-off horns came up to Judas and told him kind of quiet like that she thought they'd better get on up to the top of the rocky hill before the flood came down the creek.

Judas had heard tell about flood but it's a mighty hard idea to take in on a still, hot, dusty Sunday morning when all that was on his mind was what he was going to preach about. He studied on the idea for a while and then when the little Spanish goat told him she believed the goats were going to follow the old does with or without him he decided they'd have Sunday services on the top of the rocky hill.

Sure enough they hadn't even got to the first hymn when a wind started to blow and the sky to the northwest turned just about the color of cedar berries and the rain came down like baby frogs kicking up puffs of caliche dust clear to their knees. Pretty soon little trickles started down the rocky hill. That hand-raised goat was real inspired and he started in to tell about Noah and the ark and how he knew ahead of time about the flood just like Noah and how he'd saved them all and how thankful they ought to be.

From up on the rocky hill all the goats could see that the creek was coming up fast toward the chicken house and when the water got to running inside the chickens mostly had the daylights scared out of them and were running around in a dither and getting up on the chicken house or up in the trees, and one fool chicken sat out the whole flood on a cedar fence post. Chickens sort of can't look ahead much and they thought however it was was the way it was always going to be. So they cackled a lot and flapped their wings and complained because they thought it was way too much water and what were they going to do as their feed pans was being washed down the creek.

Old Fighter and the barn cats were up in the loft safe and dry and they made no comments except to theirselves. They were keeping an eagle eye out on the mice that had moved to various high places. Maybe they were looking out to rescue some of them later on closer to dinnertime.

There was a lot of brush and fence posts coming down the creek and even though that hand-raised goat kept on preaching he was repeating hisself a lot and most of the goats was watching the creek more than they were listening. It was the same wise old nanny who saw it first. She excused herself to Judas for speaking out and said for them to look at that coming down the creek.

All the goats were astounded. They saw such a chicken as they had never seen. Well, it wasn't a chicken, it was too big for a chicken. It sure wasn't a duck because it couldn't swim for who laid the chunk. It was rolling in the crest of the flood and yelling for help without a shred of dignity. It snagged up in the old oak tree that Judas regularly used for his pulpit, clambered up onto a big limb,

stretched itself up and shrieked for help over and over 'til the goats flapped their ears down tight and the chickens started in to cackle in alarm and the barn cats laid their heads down in the hay and put their paws up over their ears. It was only a couple of hours before the creek went back down but that bird never shut up so it seemed a lot longer.

The goats went on down to the creek and looked up at that bird in the tree and Judas climbed up to take a closer look. The bird left off yelling help and snapped at them goats about what had taken them so long to get there. He talked kind of plummy like English royalty. He told them he was an exquisite and very valuable bird and a first cousin to the head peacock at the castle of the King and Queen of England and the little princesses . . . and what was for luncheon?

A lot of his feathers were missing and about half of what was left was bent, but, sopping wet and all, when he spread out his tail even the cats were amazed. The chickens were especially impressed. They kept telling each other that he was first cousin to the peacock King and Queen of England and the little princesses. Whenever they found a really good bug they'd spit it out right at his feet just in hope he'd eat it as a favor to them. They were so proud to know royalty.

Judas made up a special sermon about how

Kings are specially chosen to rule and the King of Heaven picks out Kings for the world and that's how come they know so much and get more than everbody else. The peacock would interrupt whenever he thought of it and correct the goat's grammar and pronunciation, which didn't go down too good with the preacher.

Everthing had to be just so to please the peacock. He had to be called your Highness and your Excellency. He had to have the most comfortable perch and first choice at everthing to eat because he had a more delicate palate than them. "I am elegant, am I not? Magnificent, wouldn't you say so?" He'd stretch his neck to look at hisself 'til Judas was starting in to mutter about separation of Church and State.

My aunt and uncle and the children didn't get back 'til late because the road was washed out. Uncle Orville right away knew that peacock had to belong to the boys up the way whose daddy owned the bank so he called them and they came on down and got their bird as soon as the mojados had got the lane fixed.

It had got to be pretty much of a strain on everbody, entertaining royalty. I'll tell you, they were all glad to see them tail feathers heading in the opposite direction. My uncle said that that peacock wasn't nothing but a trumped up, high falutin', tin spoon Episcopal anyhow.

Judas and the
Great Sam Bass Treasure

MY COUSINS HAD SPENT a lot of time, like ever other child in central Texas, looking for the Great Sam Bass treasure. Sam Bass was a real true Outlaw—a train robber, a bank robber, a hold-up man. He'd stole all kinds of money and gold and jewelry and it wasn't ever found. Everbody knew how he'd hid it in a limestone cave somewheres between Sabinal and Round Rock. Everbody in Gillespie and Kerr and Mason on over to Travis Counties knows about it and they all hope to find it so they don't tell about it much. They just keep looking.

That summer after the flood my uncle said he'd sure like to find it because the flood had put him back some and the bank wouldn't count the Sam Bass treasure as collateral till he'd found it.

The flood had not only knocked down a bunch of fences but it had also rearranged some land. The pecan bottom was all broke up and about one half of the orchard had gone down the gravelly creek to the Pedernales.

One Sunday morning Judas was preaching away up on a big limestone outcrop up on rocky hill. He was going on about the Cardinal's virtues of poverty, chastity, obedience, gluttony, vanity and vain glory, when by some Billy Sunday mis-step, the rock he was preaching from got turned over and old Judas stepped down into a hole that was about fifteen feet deep. When the rocks stopped raining in on his head he looked up at the ceiling and commenced to cry out about how he was trapped and he wasn't never going to get out and how he was too young to die and some other things that nobody would want repeated before ladies and little kids.

Some of the goats thought they should go get the mojados to get Judas out, so they went on back to the feed lot to look for them but when they got there the little children was having a nanny-berry pitching contest at each other and the goats got so interested in that that they forgot what they came for.

The little Spanish goat and some of the old nannies kept talking to Judas and pretty soon they got him to where he'd listen to sense. They told him to get up off the floor and to look around for a way out. But he couldn't. You see, ever time he'd stand up another one of them old canvas sacks would bust open and coins would scatter all over the place and he'd fall

down again. I mean, he didn't say that, he didn't have any more idea of the great Sam Bass treasure than he did of the Vatican.

Finally, poor old Judas started in to cry and he said, "Oh please, Little Sugar Foot." (I hadn't ever told you he called her that because I didn't want you to think less of him on account of it, but he did.) "Oh please, Little Sugar Foot, get me out of here," and he busted out crying like he hadn't cried since his momma died.

The little Spanish goat told him to lay still and think about his next sermon. She sure knew how to quieten him down. So that goat laid down there on the great Sam Bass treasure and thought about Jacob sleeping on stones and dreaming about a ladder. He got pretty excited and told the little Spanish goat to go get him a ladder. She sighed and rolled her eyes at the other nannies and told him to think some more.

So he thought about Joseph in the dry well and Daniel in the lions' den.

The wise old doe with the broken-off horns had stood by old Judas in his hour of need and it was her that said, "Judas, dear, do you notice there's a lot of breeze coming up out of this hole? Do you suppose that means there's another opening? Could you sniff around a little?"

Judas sniffed and told the little Spanish goat that the air was probably coming through the same tunnel that the sunlight was coming through.

Slipping and sliding on all the gold coins and diamond rings and ruby and pearl necklaces, he started up a tunnel that opened out on a little bluff all grown over with mountain laurels and stickery brush. Judas squenched his eyes shut tight and scrambled out into the open.

Well, when Judas restored hisself to his congregation there was a regular jubilation. That hand-raised goat told how as soon as he saw he wasn't stove up too bad from his long fall he right away saw there was another way out and he told how desperate and dangerous the climb was up fifty feet of dark and slippery tunnel and how a wall of thorns like to of tore his eyes out. He went on about Jacob and the ladder and Joseph and his coat of many colors in the dry well and Daniel and the lions' den and how they had all been in the same fix as him. They all sang "Onward Christian Soldiers" and had a fine time.

It wasn't that easy for poor old Judas, but afterwards he limped over to that little Spanish goat and told her he sure was much obliged for her staying by him and he sure hoped someday she'd fall in a hole and he'd be there to help her. You see, he hated to be beholden.

My uncle noticed the pitiful limp that goat had in his hind foot and he held old Judas between his legs so as he could look at it and he used his pocket knife to pry a rock out from between his hooves. Well, it wasn't a rock at all but it was probably the biggest diamond in the whole great Sam Bass treasure that had got lodged in the cleft of Judas' hoof while he was struggling to get hisself on all fours.

Now the crying shame is that my uncle was more concerned with seeing to whether Judas' foot was hurt than with the rock so he just sort of pitched it over his shoulder toward the chicken house. All the chickens hustled over to see if it was manna from heaven and one of them must of swallowed it because when my uncle got over there he couldn't find it again.

After that ever time the chicken house needed cleaning out he'd tell us to do it real careful because that diamond from the great Sam Bass treasure had probably just about worked its way through one of them chickens and you could never know which pile of droppings could have that diamond in it.

I remember his eyes would twinkle so that I sometimes wondered if it was a true story. But I can tell you one thing for certain, my aunt sure did have the cleanest chicken house in Gillespie County.

Invincible Ignorance

IT WAS OF A MORNING and the wise old nanny with the broken-off horn was out with her new little silky kid and the other spring kids and their mommas. They were teaching them how to eat the thistle buds without getting stickers in their lips and how to nip off the tenderest new leaves at the ends of the brush so as to get their vitamins. They were showing them where to watch out for danger and scorpions and black widows and yellow jackets and red hornets and rattlesnakes and copperheads. And they were encouraging them not to step on the horny toads or the rusty-gut lizards or the coach whips because they were good animals and they couldn't help the way they looked. They were instructing them not to eat the bloat weed because that would give them belly aches. And not to tromp around in the water before they drank or they'd be drinking muddy water.

Meanwhile Judas and Old Slick were leaning up against the big oak by the creek watching a water moccasin swim by and discussing theology and the deplorable ignorance of the congregation about the Holy Scriptures. Old Slick said that if they never learned to read they would never learn any part of the wisdom of the Scriptures. He told Judas that they better hurry up and get the young goats taught how to read before they got too old to learn how. He pulled off a real sad face and told Judas that it was just too bad they was too old to learn to read theirselves. "Why, son, we'd be the most renowned preachers in all of Gillespie county . . . ." Like he said, they had plenty of fire, they just lacked learning.

That evening Judas told the wise old nanny what a fine plan he had for the little kids. He was going to have a school for all the young goats so as they could learn to read the Scriptures. They could be taught theology and spirituality and things like that better when they could read and do sums.

The wise old doe didn't usually argue with Judas. If there wasn't going to be any harm done she just kept her own counsel.

But Judas started in about how it was the old nannies who was the ones that was going to do the teaching and how he and Slick was going to be the ones who was going to tell them what it was they were supposed to teach and how fast. Well, that wise old nanny looked at him and Old Slick first with one eye and then the other and she swallowed down her cud for future rumination, and she told him square out that it was going to have to be him, hisself teaching them does and nannies how to read cause that was going to be the only way that they would know how. And, maybe he should just cut out the middle man and do the teaching hisself, him and Slick. Judas looked like he might be going to drop the whole subject.

Along about this same time my uncle had let the shaving cream people put up a set of signs on the posts of the road fence. The signs were just beautiful, all fresh painted, blue and yellow and real clear lettering in the middle of ever little sign. The set my uncle got said:

> He loved his horse
> But not his cooking;
> He now has a wife
> Who's better looking.
> Burma Shave.

We all thought the signs were pretty hilarious and my uncle said he'd like to rent out the rest of his fence posts.

The goats studied on these signs for a long time till most of them lost interest and they couldn't make a particle of sense out of any of it anyway. Judas never gave up considering those signs until he had them by heart. He kept on looking at them, first with one eye and then another, hoping that it would come to him what they meant. Then one day it did. He called in all them goats together and he said he was going to read them signs to them and they were to pay close attention.

"Now you all study on this sign:

    'Bless-ed are them that don't eat thistles
    on Fridays, for they don't get stickers in
    their lips.'

and this one it says:

    'Bless-ed are them that don't eat the
    bloat weed
    for they won't get belly-aches.'

Now, this one says:

    'Bless-ed are them that don't muddy up
    the creek,
    for they will drink clear water.'

And that one there says:

    'Bless-ed are them that listens to a good
    preacher
    for they would be wise.' "

Judas was having a hard time thinking what was on all them signs and it was a good while that they stood looking at that last one. Them goats knew it was important and that they were going to have to learn to read ever last one of them signs and it was beginning to add up to a pretty long assignment. Everbody was relieved and glad when he told them that last one said:

    "Naa - amen."

The little goats had a pretty easy time learning to read the signs on the fence posts and they could recite them off just about any day. And they got them

all right as rain too, except for the one about listening
to the preacher, well the little Spanish goat had
taught them little goats to say:

> "Bless-ed are them that listens to a
> wise preacher
> for they would be good."

Old Judas never did set her straight on that.
Maybe he liked it better that way.

Anyway, no more was heard about the school
project. And even now, most early mornings, you can
find the nannies out with their kids teaching them
how to eat the thistle buds without getting stickers
in their lips and how to get their vitamins and where
to watch out for danger and scorpions and black
widows and rattlesnakes, and not to step on the horny
toads and other good animals that can't help the way
they look, and not to eat the bloat weed or tromp
around in the water before they drink.

Wars and Rumors of Wars

IT WAS A REAL wet spring and came kind of late but turned hot right off. Everbody said it was too wet to plow and too hot to dance so there'd probably be a lot of July weddings.

It was that same spring that there was an awful pack of dogs that had been good dogs once but they had left their homes and forgotten their responsibilities and gone wild in a pack. They were bird dogs and retrievers and sheep dogs and rat terriers and even a dachshund. They'd all gone bad. They lived by their rough wits and hunted and caught what they could to eat. And it wasn't always jack rabbits . . . they were roaming the county it was said, getting into everbódy's pastures and killing lambs and kids and even pulling down a calf once in a great while. Everbody was telling about it and, what was worse, everbody was believing it. And furthermore, everbody was worried half sick because there was stories all around about how they'd all been bit by rabid bats or had a fight with a rabid skunk and they all had hydrophobia.

Everbody was on the lookout for those dogs.

My uncle had told the mojados to keep the goats in sight all the time and he gave them a loaded double-barreled shotgun for protection. It was the mojados that had the sense to warn old Judas and his little Billy the kid (the one that Uncle Demi John had helped to birth) and old Slick the show goat about the peril of attack they faced.

Judas realized them goats didn't know the first thing about defense. Suppose that pack of vicious dogs was to get into the back pasture and get after them? Them goats wouldn't stand half a chance. So, him and little Billy and Slick and some of the other big bucks of the herd had a big strategy meeting. They decided what they needed was a dedicated, trained and ready standing home guard, just in case them feral dogs ever made a move on them.

They had regular butting practice so as they could butt them wild dogs clean out of their pasture. Old Slick did all the battle commands like "Forward march!" and "Advance to the enemy!" and "Present Horns!" He had big plans for hisself about being an officer, but Judas pulled the damper on that, saying he couldn't be an officer and clergy too. But Slick thought there wasn't anything in the Bible that said that and he told Judas the Maccabees were priests and officers too, and that Judas was being unreasonable. So Judas told them other goats to call him Chaplain.

In the early morning, when the goats went up the rocky hill, Slick said they were going on bivouac and to keep their eyes peeled for them feral dogs. He'd post pickets at observation points and they were supposed to say, "Who goes there?" to any dogs that they saw. Old Slick hisself scouted the perimeters till he wore a pathway along the fence line. He hollered, "Halt, who goes there!" to so many jack-rabbits that they got to where they'd come line up just to watch him do it.

That evening it was raining pretty hard and my aunt had the little Spanish goat up on the back porch at milking time. My uncle was telling how old Groosmacher had shot one of his own goats on account of he had mistook it for a feral dog. And when my aunt told Carley John to get his bicycle and take a fruit-jar full of goat milk over to Mrs. Enderle while it was still warm because her new baby had the colic and that was the best thing for it, my uncle said he'd drive him over in the pick-up because them feral dogs might pull him down off his bicycle and tear him all to pieces. When my uncle came out the screen door with his gun, my aunt was wrapping a clean dish rag around the fruit-jar and she said for him to be sure and not shoot anything that had horns.

Well, when the little Spanish goat told all of that to Judas, he said, "Saints deliver us! We're going to get caught in the crossfire." And he called a special prayer meeting. Old Slick, who had given himself a field commission to Sheriff because that was the highest rank he knew about, said that he couldn't stay around because he had to scout the perimeters for infiltrators.

Then Judas started in on how this was going to be war, and they all knew he'd always preached against war and told how unhealthy it was for living things, but that this war was going to be different because this was going to be a just war and them goats was on the side of right and since they had faith as big as a mustard seed it would probably be a mighty shield to them and anyway the earth would very likely open up and swaller up them iniquitous feral dogs like the Red Sea had swallered up the Pharaoh's soldiers. He declared that they didn't need to be afraid, because it wasn't going to be the end of everthing if they'd just do their duty and be brave and true like old Slick and follow his orders and stand fast when the time came and they'd win to Victory. Then they sang all four verses of "Battle Hymn of the Republic."

Meanwhile you just can't imagine the distress and consternation of that show goat when he found the far back fence busted down and the whole pack of them wild dogs coming at him up the backside of the rocky hill with Old Fencebuster, the outlaw goat, outdistancing them easy by a hundred yards. Poor old Slick just felt all his courage melting away, just oozing out of him. He couldn't call to mind a single battle command to yell. When Old Fencebuster hollered at him to run and called him a dern fool, old Slick saw the wisdom of a strategic withdrawal. He took off like a shot out of a cannon for that prayer meeting.

Them dogs had learned a few hard bought lessons about herd courage and when Slick and Old Fencebuster came skidding into that prayer meeting and Slick screamed, "Present horns! To the enemy!" that pack of dogs whined some and milled around for a while with the sweat dripping off their tongues, but they didn't offer to renew hostilities.

Now, the mojados had seen the whole thing but they had laid the loaded double-barreled shotguns down real careful on account of they were laughing so they were afraid they'd shoot theirselves. When later on they would tell about it it was hard to get the gist of it because they'd start in laughing again at the memory of how it was just old Martinez's female dog which was feeling real romantic and them misnamed wild dogs were just a bunch of her boyfriends courting her for her favors.

How Old Fencebuster
Got Born Again

AFTER THE FERAL DOGS had all gone back to their homes and taken up their responsibilities again, that old outlaw goat, Fencebuster, decided to stay with the herd. He was sort of a hero to the other goats and they wanted him to stay and lend them the hard-won wisdom that he had got from all his days of traveling around being an outlaw. So, like I said, Old Fencebuster decided to stay. It was getting on toward Fall, and it appeared he sort of took a shine to that wise old nanny with the broken-off horns.

His coat was so dirty and full of burrs and it smelled so bad that when the mojados sheared him they just took it out and buried it. He had a fine long heavy beard and out of respect they left the beard. They dipped him and washed him and doctored him and trimmed up his hooves and oiled them and he looked about like an old time cowboy coming out of a barber shop. The mojados liked him.

They called him El Macho Grande.

The wise old doe had always been popular with all the goats so it wasn't like she was flummoxed or embarrassed by the coarse attentions that Old Fencebuster paid her court with. Actually he was sort of a celebrity and she thought it was nice to be fancied. They were seen together a good bit and there was some gossipy talk by some of the younger does about her being taken in by an old outlaw who was playing at being tamed and she should stop being silly and act her age.

"Well, time will tell," was all the wise old doe would say and Judas said pretty much the same thing, "Well, time will tell." And it did, sure enough.

That old outlaw goat put on such a face of respectability as you wouldn't of known him if you'd of been his momma. You'd of thought he was a visiting preacher at least. Whenever Judas would preach, Old Fencebuster would holler "AHMEN!" at the end of ever sentence and sometimes right in the middle. He'd beat Slick to the punch ever time. He hollered, "AHMEN!" so loud and so often that Judas got a twitch in his eye lids, that wouldn't hardly ever go away, like he was winking at everbody, which didn't add a whole lot to his sermons, and gave some of the younger goats the giggles.

The mojados didn't have a whole lot to entertain theirselves with, if you don't count work, so they were taking bets all around on how long El Macho Grande would last as a fenced-in, tame ranch goat, even with the companionship of the wise old doe to keep him in line.

He got to where he knew the words to all the hymns and sang out real loud with lots of spirit. He seemed a little hard of hearing or at least he must not of been able to hear pitch, which is real unusual in a goat, but may have been because of the rough life that he had lived. The poor little Spanish goat had got to where she took a lot of pride in the hymn singing and sometimes she'd just about cry when Old Fencebuster would drown out all her special harmonies she had worked up.

The wise old doe said that he had the spirit and maybe his ears would be opened one day like the pilgrim from Samaria but that in the meantime it would be good if the little Spanish goat would just stick to real simple hymns.

Days went by and that Old Fencebuster began to look longingly at the horizon. The hills were calling him, his old trails and old ways. He was getting restless and the lazy days in company of the gentle wise old doe were losing some of their luster compared to the glitter of remembered adventures. And the mojados' betting odds were getting heavier till nobody would place anything on his staying.

It was of a Sunday morning, the mojados found

the fence down just where they had figured it would be, and Old Fencebuster was gone. They grinned at each other and paid up.

Judas and the little Spanish goat were both sort of shame-faced because they were more than a little glad of his being gone from prayer meeting and hymn-singing. Several of the younger nannies huddled together and allowed as how you can't teach an old dog new tricks and they thought they'd sure said something new.

But the wise old doe, she chuckled and smiled and said, "Oh, he'll be back if we ever need him. Right now he's fired up with the mission spirit, and when he busts down some other goats' fences, well, he'll go to preaching and they'll give him for love gifts what he used to have to steal. Now, ain't it better to hold a revival than a robbery?"

Old Fighter
and the Convent Cat

MY UNCLE ORVILLE used to say that if there was anything to reincarnation he sure wanted to come back as a convent cat. The nuns at Our Lady of Poverty High School had a pet cat named Daisy that was the most spoilt cat in the county. All the nuns hadn't ever had any children to love, so they just poured it onto that Daisy. That cat had got her own way about just about everthing all her life.

At the same time she was a very devout and pious cat. She went to Mass ever morning with the sisters and she knew all the liturgy better than Father Hubert. He said if he was to make one little slip she'd right away stop purring and frown at him and flick her tail in disapproval. She never ate meat on Fridays and once they'd burned up the palms and passed out the ashes for Lent she wouldn't touch a bite of meat till Easter.

Now Daisy was your basic black cat, except she

had big white ears and a bib of white under her chin like a caul and wimple and they had got her a little collar with a medal to Saint Agatha that sort of finished off the picture, so that she looked pretty much like the rest of the Sisters of Divine Inspiration that taught at the High School. But she had that kind of prideful look that some nuns get on account of they know more about Christian Love than anybody else.

Well, what happened was that the principal of the school, sweet old Sister Saint Jerome, God rest her soul, was getting on in years. We figured she must of been close to ninety-five because she'd had her diamond jubilee back when my aunt and uncle were still in school. Well, she sort of keeled over one day when she was about to spank one of the eighth grade boys for his sins. She had just told him to bend over the desk but he must of been hard of hearing because he dropped his pants down instead. My uncle said she had a smile on her face but my aunt said that she did not, that she used to be a nursing sister.

Well, anyhow, the motherhouse sent up a new principal, Sister Mary Torquemada. She had the hay fever. Almost everthing in nature made her sneeze, but especially a cat. If a cat was anywheres around she'd get hay fever bad and it would make her meaner than she already was, which was saying something. So, of course, Verleen and Carley John and all the little children brought that convent cat out to the ranch that same day, as Sister had told them it would be all right with my aunt and uncle because they were good Catholics. And that's how the convent cat happened to come to the ranch and meet up with Old Fighter, the famous five-at-a-time mouse-catching tom cat.

Daisy was used to a finer life and was sure that she needed to live inside the house but my uncle said the house was no place for livestock, so Daisy took up residence on the back porch and only left it to hunt or to hear Judas preach. She was taken with his preaching and dearly loved to sing the hymns.

The first time Old Fighter laid eyes on Daisy with her little white wimple and her convent ways, he kind of sauntered up to her switching his tail and allowed as how she could be part of his harem. He was used to having as many wives as he wanted because all the momma cats wanted just such a fine old tried and true mouser to sire their litters. Daisy told him she had taken a vow of chastity so he could just peddle his wares somewheres else. It had been so long since Old Fighter had been turned down that he went into a fit of the sulks and it put his aim off so bad and he was missing so many mice that my uncle said he must of lost his interest in sport hunting.

It was right about then that Old Fighter started seriously courting that convent cat. He fancied hisself a tenor and almost ever night he'd devote some time to serenading the back porch. This didn't go down too

good with my aunt and uncle, not to speak of Judas
and the rest of the goats who didn't like to have their

sleep disturbed. Fortunately, when Old Fighter saw it wasn't having the desired effect, he left that off and started in showing off in front of Daisy ever chance he got. He'd make long perilous leaps from the mustang grape vines on the shinny oaks over onto the roof of the old outhouse. When he looked to see if she was impressed at all, she'd be licking her paws like it was the most natural thing in the world for a cat to leap a new world record ever day. He jumped on the back of a visiting dog and rode him down like a rodeo champion and when he asked her how she liked the way he'd whupped up on that dog, she told him she abhorred violence. Old Fighter even fell to the place where he started in bringing the tenderest, prettiest little mice he caught to lay on the porch steps for her. She told him she liked her mice fresh caught and she would do fine hunting her own, thank you very much.

Judas knew it was a desperate case when Old Fighter started showing up for prayer meeting on a regular basis. When he came to see Judas about a general confession, Judas saw that something had to be said.

First off he quoted to Old Fighter all about everthing coming to him who waits and to possess his soul in patience. He told him that for everthing there was a season, and a time for ever purpose under heaven. Old Judas told that cat there was a time to embrace and a time to refrain from that kind of thing.

He told him about a season to put in the seed and a season for growing and a season for birth and a season for rejoicing and that Old Fighter just had to possess himself in patience and wait 'til she came into season and to quit making such a dern fool of himself.

And it happened just like Judas had said it would. One evening Old Fighter detected a scent on the wind that he recognized from of old, and he started in with his best song all about soft grass in a secluded place perfumed with love that would never die. He swaggered along switching his tail in great sweeping arcs and not even looking behind him, and sure enough he hadn't got half way to his favorite hideout 'til Daisy had caught up to him. She was coy and shy but she realized she was in love and any promises she had made to the Sisters of Divine Inspiration were forgotten. Old Fighter kept her time pretty well tied up for the next few days and she seemed real pleased about it.

It wasn't too long after that that she had a fine litter of kittens under the kitchen sink and it was a while before Old Fighter got to see them, but one day she took them out for the air and he admired them a lot. Two little yellow toms just like him and one pretty little black female with a white wimple on her front. But you should have seen them other cats sniggering behind their paws. How, they wanted to know, could Old Fighter account for them two calicoes?

How Judas Saw the Strangers
and Took Them In

AFTER THE GOATS' COATS were redeemed for
such a fine sum, my uncle Orville looked forward to
good times. Mohair seemed like a sure investment.
Him and the mojados built an extension on the winter
quarter and my uncle bought himself some new goats
to increase and improve his herd. These new goats
were some kind of special breed from Arabia or some-
place and they had fine, long, silky hair that almost
dragged the ground.

Now, if you're going to improve a herd you
want the new goats to sire all the kids. So the old
goats have to get fixed up so as they can't be the
sires. After that, old Judas pretty much had to give
up on romance.

And to make matters worse them new goats
weren't even practicing Catholics. Naturally that
hand-raised goat named them pagans, and
heatherns, and infidels. He pointed out how they

110

didn't look right and they smelled strange and foreign and kind of skunky.

The first evening that Judas felt up to it they had a prayer meeting down by the creek and those new goats wanted to come along. Well, old Judas curled up his lip and sniffed at their skunky coats and right out said he didn't want his parishioners associating with ignorant foreigners and he declared also as how they hadn't been invited to be part of his congregation. He talked right up to the biggest buck goat and he said, "Boy, just take your goats and git." And they did.

He preached at his goats about purity and keeping Texas for Texans. He reminded them how bad times got when they had let in all them Yankee goats. He got on them a bunch about not fraternizing with strangers. He explained about chastity and the holiness of celibacy. He snorted and exhorted against their immoral natures, the occasions of sin, about giving scandal by associating with goats of low character, and he described the steep, narrow and stickery trail a goat had to climb to get up the hillside of virtue to its pinnacle: chastity.

Since right then none of the does was in season the goats listened and chewed and flapped their ears and were not troubled in their consciences. They were by nature refined and decorous, although not inclined toward abstinence. Mostly they were thinking about what was for supper.

The prayer meeting was finished off with some fine hymn-singing about being the favorite herd of the pastures, and then they headed on back to the yard to see what they might could find to eat. And, do you know, them foreign goats had got fed while the rest of them was down at the creek paying for their sins. It was enough to make a preacher cuss.

There in front of the new winter quarter them foreign goats were eating a stack of the most delicate fine-stemmed grass and clover, fresh-dried and still green. They was scarfing it up like they was the only goats on the place.

"Greedy heatherns! Selfish pagans! Gluttonous infidels!" Old Judas took off at them foreign goats like a shot out of a cannon. Like he said later, "If them no good, outlandish, feed-rustling, greedy-gut foreigners hadn't of backed off so sudden I'd of butted them clean out of Gillespie County." As it was, he butted right through the middle of that stack and came out with grass stems and clover all caught in his horns like Christmas decorations. That made even some of the wise old does laugh, which was embarrassing to him.

It appeared, though, to some of the goats—and my uncle always said it was so—that just before Judas charged, them foreign goats had turned

around so as they could face to the East, toward Austin. Then they had got down on their front knees to say their prayers. You see, as it turned out, they were real religious goats and five times ever day they had to say their prayers. And when they started in to praying it was in some foreign tongue. Judas pricked up his ears. "Listen to them goats speaking in tongues," he said. Right away Old Slick, that show goat that had been a sorry rustler but who had come into the fold, joined in with them. He didn't want to be behind the door when them other goats was getting all the glory. My uncle said everbody was surprised at Old Slick speaking in tongues but most of all them foreign goats.

Now, I'll tell you, old Judas was mightily impressed with the idea of having parishioners who had prayer meetings five or so times ever day. So he went ahead and got up a sermon on seeing the strangers and taking them in. It was a pretty good sermon and with the does coming on into season his flock took it up more and more zealously.

After a while the mojados got around to clipping the long skunky hair off them foreign goats, and under all that hair they looked pretty near like any other goats. After some time they smelled about as right as a buck goat ever can. The does seemed to find them pretty romantic and Judas got to be quick as a duck on a June bug at solemnizing their unions. His

114

bell clanked like a wedding bell all up and down the rocky hill as the hazy warm days of romance and frolic eased by.

For a while they mostly still called them "them foreign goats," and then it was "them other goats," and at last just "us goats." One quiet peaceful Sunday morning all the goats went down to the gravelly creek and Judas, that hand-raised, priest-bishop-mullah goat poured creek water on the newcomers and made them official Texans.

Moral Turpitude

MY UNCLE HAD let my cousin Carley John enter old Slick, that show goat, in the Fat Stock Show and he had come away with a blue ribbon. Everbody was so proud of it that they hung it right up over the mantle piece beside Grandma's certificate she received from Governor Hogg for having seven sons for the Southland. I never thought that winning that ribbon was what made Old Slick get after Judas, but it did all happen soon after that.

That show goat, who hadn't ever been anything but a loyal, right-thinking, communicating parishioner before, just climbed up on a low bluff right in front of the whole herd and started in. He went into how it was that he had been such a sorry, low-down, two-bit, no-good, tin-horn, conniving, rustler on account of he had been led astray and through no fault of his own. He had always tried to live right to the best as he knew how and it was just that he'd fallen in with real bad company and never had a chance and he shouldn't be judged hard on

116

account of that. Now that he had seen the right and true way, he just had to speak out against sin when he saw it no matter who it was and he had to tell everbody about the sins of others whenever he had half a chance.

It was one of those days that will live in infamy. That show goat had a high-pitched voice and when he raised it so as all the goats could hear, it sort of screeched on their ears. He started in telling about Judas' romance with the blue-ribbon nanny at the Knights of Columbus Festival. You see the same blue-ribbon nanny had been at the Fat Stock Show. When she'd heard that Slick was from Judas' herd, she asked him how Judas was feeling and told him what a fine job he'd done at the Knights of Columbus Festival, and was Judas there she'd like to renew acquaintance with him. She didn't mean a bit of harm. That's the way things come out sometimes.

"Fornications!" that show goat hollered and his ears flopped around like everthing and landed over his eyes. And looking out from behind his ears he went on to tell about it all in such a way that it sounded like the worst kind of thing.

The goats were sort of intrigued. They coughed up their cuds and raised up their eyebrows and flagged their tails up and down and they looked at that show goat with first one eye and then the other and then they looked at Judas. Now Judas didn't know which way to look so he started in to

117

whine and cry. "I have sinned. I have sinned." His lower lip trembled and big old crocodile tears ran down his face and dropped off his beard.

Then old Slick started in on Judas' old love affair with the little Spanish goat, and Judas was tuning up to cry some more.

But that was where the show goat made his big miscalculation. That billy kid that the little Spanish goat had raised up so gentle, yes sir, children, that little kid got a good running start and he butted that show goat right in the rump. Now, Slick wasn't looking for that surprise and he took off the bluff like a turkey trying to learn how to fly.

"You cain't talk that away about my momma!" hollered Billy.

That show goat finished flying through the air and then did a summersalt and it looked like he had about eight legs, they were pumping the air so fast.

That little billy goat spread his legs out and stood up on the bluff and he told them goats how bad and sinful it was of that old Slick to speak false witness against his momma and his daddy, Judas. Why, Slick wasn't even on the place back then. And what a sorry thing to of told on that lady goat at the Knights of Columbus Festival when it was only hearsay, and how anybody who hadn't never sinned could chunk the first rock.

That little Billy said that there wasn't a truth-

fuller goat in all Gillespie county than their own
Judas priest, and it seemed like they must be awful
ungrateful if they couldn't hardly remember how he'd
rassled the devil machine nor gone out missionarying
nor how he'd delivered them from Lent nor how he'd
saved them when they all got rustled.

Judas, who had been all downcast, began to
swell up with pride and he trotted up on to the little
bluff with his little Billy. He was thinking to preach
some too—but when he looked out where his congregation was supposed to be, all he saw was that
sorry show goat wobbling his head and still trying
to get up on all fours. The wise old nanny with the
broken-off horns was taking the rest of the goats
down to the gravelly creek, which was running
again, to get a drink and they was saying to each
other how it was better not to encourage that sort
of thing.

Judas looked at that discombobulated show
goat and then at his little Billy and he allowed as
how it was just the two of them but they might as
well do a healing service for poor old Slick. So they
did some petitions and some laying on of hooves and
pretty soon they were able to go on down to the
creek for evening services so the show goat could
testify.

That little Billy leaned up against his momma
and it was a beautiful sight to see them looking up at

Judas in the old oak tree while they all sang together:
        "Peace will rain, peace will rain,
        Feed will grow in peaceful rain.
        Gentle sun, gentle sun,
        Feed will grow in gentle sun.
        Quiet nights, quiet nights,
        Sleep will come in quiet nights."

Amen.